Homework Helpers

Science

Ages 7–8
Key Stage 2 / Year 3

Andy Bailey, Jane Harris
& Michael Wilkinson

 *We're the Homework Helpers!*

 We've thought up lots of fun activities for you!

 *So grab your pens and pencils...*

 ...and let's get started!

Longman

An imprint of **Pearson Education**

Harlow, England · London · New York · Reading, Massachusetts · San Francisco
Toronto · Don Mills, Ontario · Sydney · Tokyo · Singapore · Hong Kong · Seoul
Taipei · Cape Town · Madrid · Mexico City · Amsterdam · Munich · Paris · Milan

Series editors:
Stuart Wall & Geoff Black
With thanks to Jane Webster for additional material

These people helped us write the book!

A complete range of **Homework Helpers** is available.

		ENGLISH	MATHS	SCIENCE
Key Stage 1	Ages 5–6 Year 1	✓	✓	Science is not included in the National Tests at Key Stage 1
	Ages 6–7 Year 2	✓	✓	
Key Stage 2	Ages 7–8 Year 3	✓	✓	✓
	Ages 8–9 Year 4	✓	✓	✓
	Ages 9–10 Year 5	✓	✓	✓
	Ages 10–11 Year 6	✓	✓	✓

This tells you about all our other books.

Which ones have you got?

Pearson Education Limited
Edinburgh Gate, Harlow
Essex CM20 2JE, England
and Associated Companies throughout the world

First published 2000

British Library Cataloguing in Publication Data
A catalogue entry for this title is available from the British Library

ISBN 0-582-38152-5

Printed in Great Britain by Ashford Colour Press Ltd, Gosport, Hampshire

This is for grown-ups!

Guidance and advice

Schools are now asked to set regular homework, even for young children. Government guidelines for Year 3 (ages 7–8) suggest $1\frac{1}{2}$ hours of homework a week. Children are also encouraged to do at least 10–20 minutes of reading each day.

Experimental and investigative science

The aim of the National Curriculum for science is to develop children's knowledge of scientific ideas, processes and skills, and relate these to everyday experiences. Teachers provide opportunities for children to make predictions, plan experiments, learn how to make their test fair, record results, consider evidence, and then think about their results and the effectiveness of the experiment.

All the activities in this book are written to complement the National Curriculum. The emphasis is on short, enjoyable activities designed to stimulate a child's interest in science. Each activity will take 10–20 minutes, depending on the topic, and the amount of drawing and colouring.

Themes and topics

Throughout the book key words have been set in **bold** text – these highlight the themes and content of the activities, and provide a guide to the topics covered.

Encourage your child

Leave your child to do the activity on their own, but be available to answer any questions. Try using phrases like: That's a good idea! How do you think you could do it? What happens if you do it this way? These will encourage your child to think about how they could answer the question for themselves.

If your child is struggling …

Younger children might need help understanding the question before they try to work out an answer, and children who need help with reading or writing may need you to work with them. If your child is struggling with the writing, ask them to find the answer and then write it in for them. Remember, even if your child gets stuck, be sure to tell them they are doing well.

The activities start on the next page! Have you got your pens and pencils ready?

Check the answers together

When they have done all they can, sit down with them and go through the answers together. Check they have not misunderstood any important part of the activity. If they have, try to show them why they are going wrong. Ask them to explain what they have done, right or wrong, so that you can understand how they are thinking.

You will find answers to the activities at the back of this book. You can remove the last page if you think your child might look at the answers before trying an activity. Sometimes there is no set answer because your child has been asked for their own ideas. Check that your child's answer is appropriate and shows they have understood the question.

Be positive!

If you think your child needs more help with a particular topic try to think of some similar but easier examples. You don't have to stick to the questions in the book – ask your own: Did you like that? Can you think of any more examples? Have a conversation about the activity. Be positive, giving praise for making an effort and understanding the question, not just getting the right answers. Your child should enjoy doing the activities and at the same time discover that learning is fun.

More on Science

There are many activities you can do outside school that will help develop your child's familiarity with science and provide valuable practice. Make sure your child has plenty of experience of weighing, measuring, observing processes and making comparisons. Look for opportunities to help your child practise predicting what will happen, collecting evidence and recording results. The more practice your child gets the more comfortable with science they will become.

Light

1 Anything that gives off light is called a **light source**. Tick the light sources shown here.

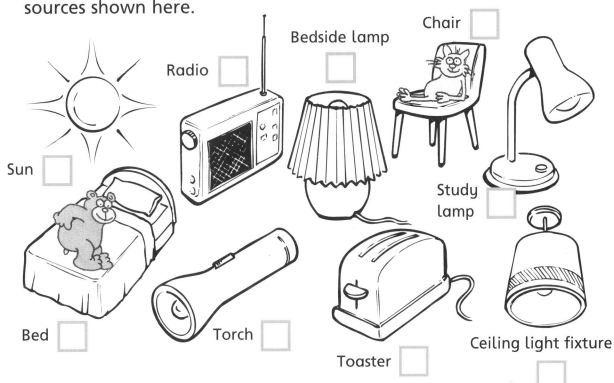

Radio ☐

Bedside lamp ☐

Chair ☐

Sun ☐

Study lamp ☐

Bed ☐

Torch ☐

Toaster ☐

Ceiling light fixture ☐

2 Light can **pass through** some things.
Which of these things will let light pass through?

Tick the boxes next to the things that will let light pass through.

Wall ☐

Window ☐

Tree ☐

Stained glass window ☐

Horse ☐

Fish bowl ☐

Box ☐

5

Shadows

When objects block the light, we get **shadows**.

1 Ask a grown-up if you can use a torch
   as a light source to form shadows of
   each of these objects.
   Draw the shape of each shadow.

You'll need to
do this activity in
a dark place!

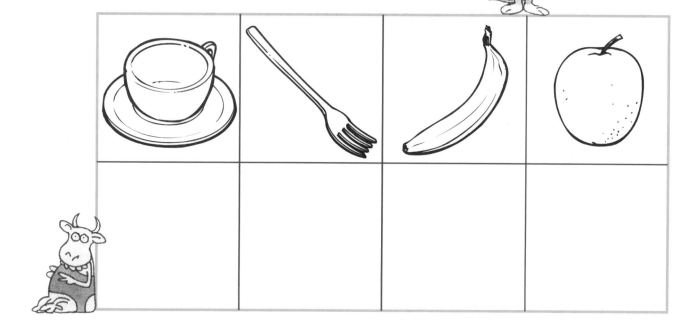

2 Try using your hands to make interesting shadows.
   Here are some ideas.

rabbit

bird

3 What is wrong with the shadow in this picture?

_____

One has been done for you.

4 The artist has left the Sun out of these pictures.
Look at the position of the shadow in each picture,
and draw the Sun in the correct place.

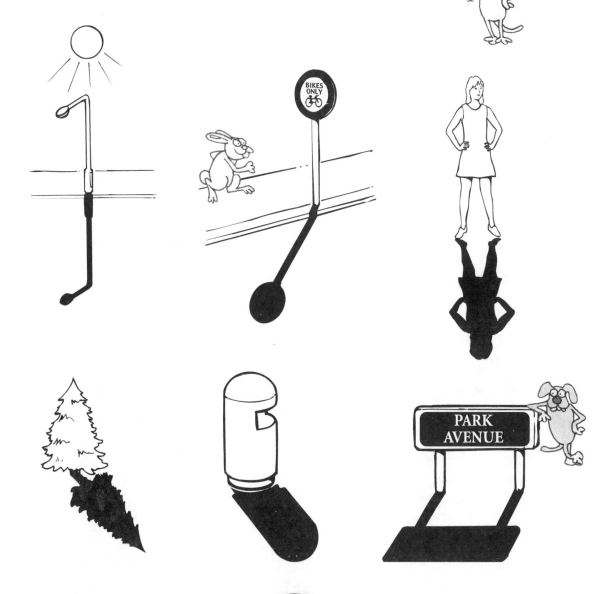

7

Shadow puppets

Yasmin and Sam have made some **shadow puppets**. They move the puppets around in front of the torch in a dark room.

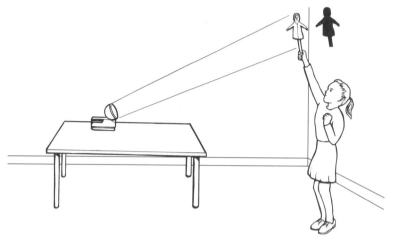

1 What do you think happens to the size of the shadow as they

move the puppet about? _____

Make your own puppet to test what will happen.

What you need

- torch or lamp as a light source
- piece of card
- blank wall to shine the shadows on

- stick
- scissors
- sticky tape

A wooden spoon will do.

What to do

1. Draw your design for your puppet shape on the piece of card.
2. Cut it out.
3. Attach it to the stick with sticky tape.
4. Set up the torch on a table so it shines on to the blank wall.
5. Hold your puppet between the torch and the wall, in the torch beam.

2 How can you change the

size of your shadow? _____

Try moving your puppet nearer to the torch and then moving it away.

3 What happened to the size of the shadow when you moved the puppet nearer to the torch?

_____

_____

4 What happened to the size of the shadow when you moved the puppet away from the torch?

_____

_____

5 Explain how the shadow of your puppet is formed.

_____

_____

True or false?

6 Some of these statements are correct (true) others are wrong (false). Put a ✓ next to the statement if you think it is true. Put a ✗ next to the statement of you think it is false.

To form a shadow puppet the light shines on the back of the puppet.

Shadows are formed when light from a source is blocked.

The shadow of an object is always the same size.

Shadows are similar shapes to the objects making them.

7 Only one of the drawings is correct. Put a ✓ beside it.

Long or short?

Did you know that the **length of shadows** changes during the day?

At the beginning and end of the day, the shadows are long.

In the middle of the day, the shadows are short.

1 Zak has been taking some photos. Which do you think he took in the middle of the day? Tick the boxes.

Zak's photos at the bottom of the page will help you work out some of the answers.

Tick the boxes next to the true statements.

2 Which of these are true?

(a) Shadows are short at midday.

(b) Shadows are long when the Sun is high in the sky.

(c) Shadows are the same length all day.

(d) Shadows are short when the Sun is high in the sky.

(e) We can use shadows to tell the time.

Shadow chart

Annie is measuring Zak's **shadow** every hour. She has written the measurements in this table.

Time	9 a.m.	10 a.m.	11 a.m.	12 o'clock	1 p.m.	2 p.m.	3 p.m.	4 p.m.
Length of shadow	70 cm	50 cm	30 cm	10 cm	30 cm	50 cm	70 cm	90 cm

Annie has started to draw a **bar chart** to show the length of Zak's shadow. Finish it off for her.

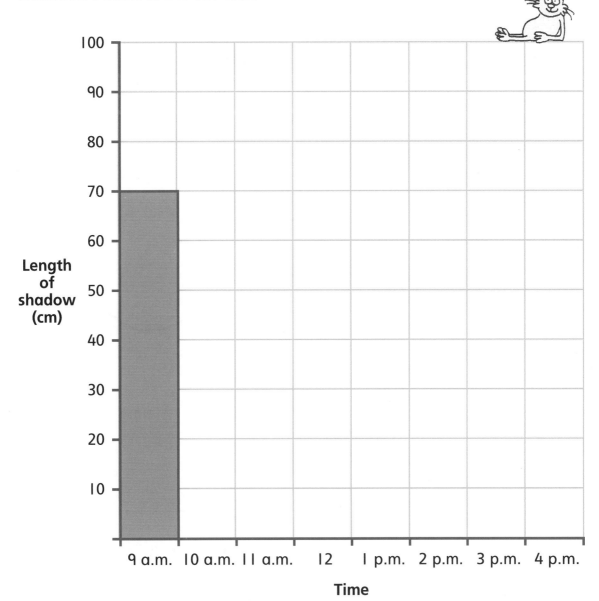

Day and night

1 Use one of these words to fill each gap.

West

East   Sun

spins

The Earth takes 24 hours to spin around once.

It is **night** when the part of the Earth where you live faces away from the Sun.

The Earth we live on _____ around. This makes it look to us as if the _____ is moving across the sky. During the day, it seems to move from _____ to _____ .

This picture shows the Earth and the Sun.

Earth

Sun

2 Is it night or day at the place marked ×? _____

3 Is it night or day at the place marked *? _____

4 Why does it become dark at the end of the day?

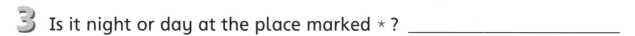

Feeding time

1 Connect each animal to the **food** it eats.

All animals need food to stay alive.

Draw a line to join the animal and its food.

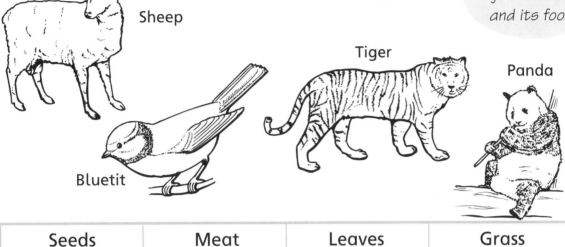

Sheep

Tiger

Panda

Bluetit

| Seeds | Meat | Leaves | Grass |

2 What do you think these animals eat? Draw a ring around the correct food in the list.

Animal	What does it eat?		
Lion	grass	meat	fish
Cow	fruit	meat	grass
Giraffe	leaves	insects	meat
Slug	insects	leaves	meat
Spider	leaves	insects	grass
Frog	grass	insects	fish
Seagull	fish	plants	leaves
Elephant	leaves	fish	meat
Goat	fruit	insects	grass
Penguin	grass	fish	leaves

3 What would happen to animals if they did not eat?

Store cupboard

1 Can you find four kinds of **fruit** in this store cupboard?

Draw a ring around each of the fruits.

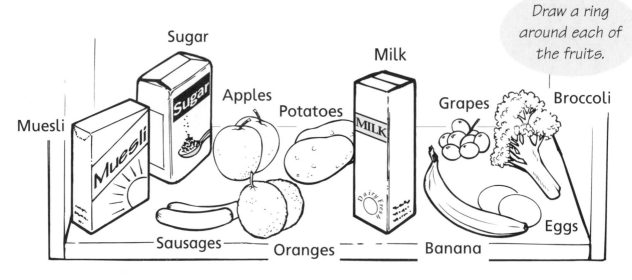

Muesli Sugar Apples Potatoes Milk Grapes Broccoli

Sausages Oranges Banana Eggs

2 Can you find five kinds of **vegetables**?

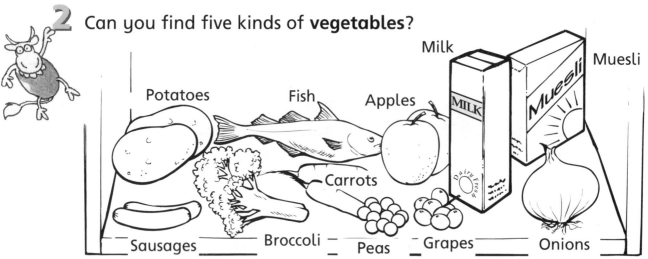

Potatoes Fish Apples Milk Muesli

Carrots

Sausages Broccoli Peas Grapes Onions

3 Can you find two kinds of **breakfast cereal**?

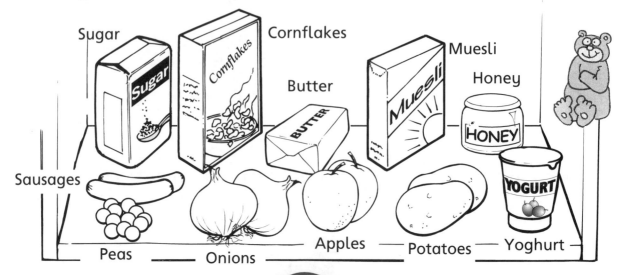

Sugar Cornflakes Butter Muesli Honey

Sausages

Peas Onions Apples Potatoes Yoghurt

4 Can you find four kinds of **dairy food**?

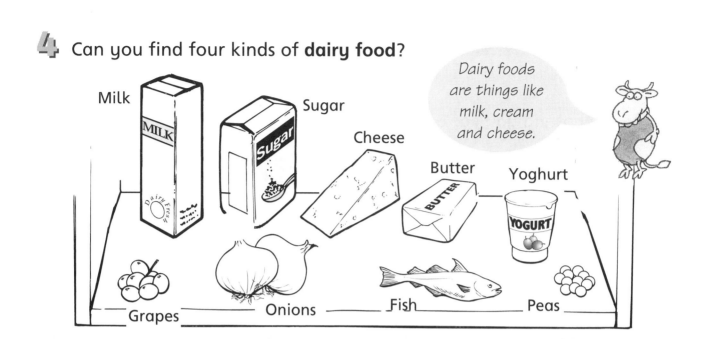

Milk

Sugar

Cheese

Butter

Yoghurt

Dairy foods are things like milk, cream and cheese.

Grapes

Onions

Fish

Peas

5 Can you find four kinds of **meat** or **fish**?

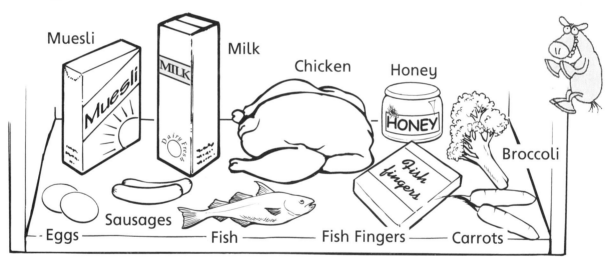

Muesli

Milk

Chicken

Honey

Broccoli

Eggs

Sausages

Fish

Fish Fingers

Carrots

6 There are two things in this cupboard that don't fit into any of the other groups. Which are they?

These things are both **sugars**.

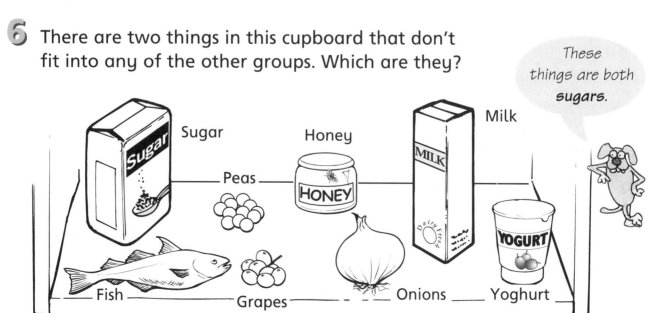

Sugar

Honey

Milk

Peas

Fish

Grapes

Onions

Yoghurt

Food of the day

1 What did you eat and drink yesterday? Make lists in the boxes.

Breakfast

Lunchtime

Evening meal

Snacks

*If an animal eats grass, we say its **diet** is grass.*

If an animal eats plants and insects, then its diet is plants and insects.

2 How is your diet different from the diet of other animals?

_____

Where do your foods come from?

How many different foods do you eat in one day?

Food for thought

Some foods help us to **grow**. Others give us **energy** to move. In this word search there are lots of words about growing and moving. Colour all the words you can find!

Here are the words to look out for.

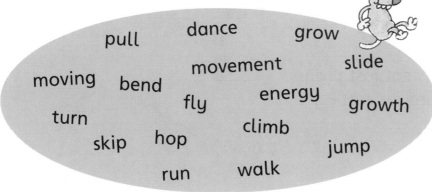

pull   dance   grow   slide   moving   bend   movement   energy   growth   fly   turn   climb   skip   hop   jump   run   walk

The words read downwards or across from left to right.

z	a	y	t	h	g	r	e	n	e	r	g	y	d
m	o	v	i	n	g	b	c	s	e	v	a	m	c
a	w	m	l	f	a	g	m	g	k	u	d	a	l
t	g	r	o	w	t	d	o	r	u	j	r	a	i
u	e	b	t	y	u	a	f	o	n	i	t	e	m
r	g	e	w	m	d	n	y	w	o	u	d	s	b
n	x	n	e	o	g	c	x	t	i	r	u	n	o
s	c	d	r	v	i	e	p	h	h	n	r	i	f
h	e	c	d	e	f	t	h	k	i	m	b	d	l
o	g	l	s	m	t	f	j	s	a	o	p	n	y
h	o	p	l	e	s	a	u	j	w	a	l	k	b
d	f	c	i	n	k	n	m	c	h	u	n	s	h
s	u	s	d	t	i	r	p	c	p	u	l	l	d
p	h	e	e	i	p	f	l	l	b	t	r	a	s

Animal teeth

Some animals eat just meat.
Their **teeth** are for stabbing and tearing.

Some animals eat just plants.
Their teeth are for cutting
and grinding.

What sort of teeth do these animals have? Draw a line
to match each animal to the correct kind of tooth.

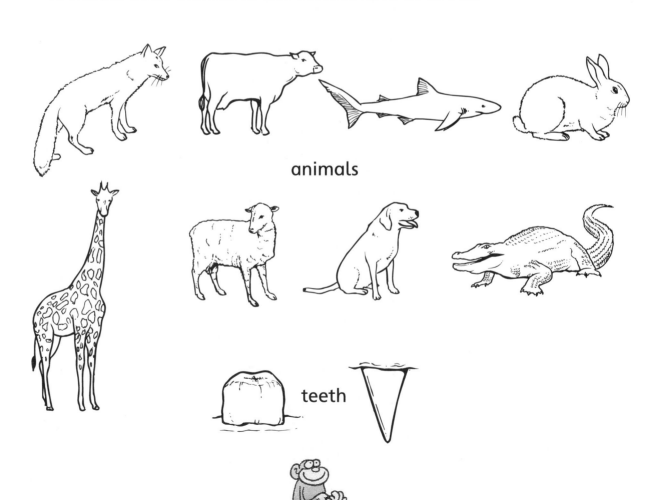

animals

teeth

Dinosaur dig

Imagine that you are looking for dinosaur bones, and you find these dinosaur **skulls**.

1 Colour the skulls of the meat-eating dinosaurs red.
Colour the skulls of the plant-eating dinosaurs green.

What clues do the skulls give you?

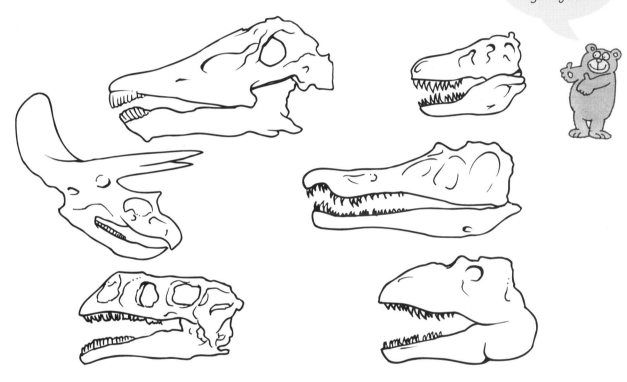

2 How did you know which skulls to colour red?

_____

_____

_____

3 How did you know which skulls belonged to plant-eating dinosaurs?

_____

_____

_____

Take a bite!

Each of these sentences has been cut in half! Draw lines to match the two halves.

New-born babies	have small milk teeth.
Young children	replace the milk teeth.
The milk teeth	are pushed out as we grow up.
Adult teeth	have no teeth.

Have you noticed that your teeth do not all look the same?

Incisors are for cutting up food.

Canine teeth are for tearing food.

Molars are for chewing food.

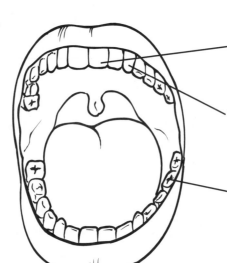

This is an **incisor**.

This is a **canine tooth**.

This is a **molar**.

Wash your hands, then feel your teeth with your tongue and your fingers.

You'll probably need to look in a mirror to answer these questions!

2 How many of your teeth are incisors? _____

3 How many are canine teeth? _____

4 How many are molars? _____

5 How many teeth do you have altogether? _____

Grit your teeth

These words describe ways of using your **teeth** to eat:

slice   crush   cut   tear   bite

grind   nibble   chew   munch

crunch   gobble   gnaw

Mime each of these ways of eating in a mirror...

... but make sure no one is watching!

Can you find all of these words in the word search?

Draw a ring around the words you find.

The words read downwards or across from left to right.

c	r	s	h	f	a	b	i	t	e	e	r	c
d	z	g	n	a	w	t	e	n	t	w	i	h
a	n	t	i	n	r	i	n	o	g	f	r	e
c	r	u	n	c	h	e	i	l	o	v	e	w
s	c	a	b	r	w	y	b	g	b	c	t	r
a	u	t	m	y	d	h	b	j	b	s	e	m
m	t	e	u	g	e	j	l	n	l	w	a	u
u	t	o	n	e	v	v	e	i	e	o	r	t
m	o	m	c	t	o	q	a	f	a	b	h	i
i	w	d	h	w	u	f	c	r	u	s	h	x
a	b	a	r	y	r	e	e	f	c	k	b	r
g	r	i	n	d	e	a	z	q	y	h	e	y
s	a	i	d	e	s	l	i	c	e	t	i	n

Good and bad

1 Some kinds of food are **bad** for your teeth. Circle the tooth-rotters here!

Sugars are bad for your teeth.

2 Which of these foods would make a **good** snack?

A good snack will not rot your teeth!

3 What three things can you do to keep your teeth and gums healthy?

_____

_____

_____

Rock hunt

1 Find all the objects in this picture that are made of **rock**. Colour them in.

2 Underneath the ground, there is rock – although in most places we cannot see it. Make a list of things that might be on top of the rock.

Houses _____ _____

_____ _____ _____

23

Rock tests

You can find out how hard a piece of rock is by trying to **scratch** it.

Annie tried this with four pieces of rock. She made a table of her results.

Type of rock	Scratches left by		
	Fingernail	Coin	Nail
Granite	No	No	No
Sandstone	No	No	Yes
Limestone	No	Yes	Yes
Chalk	Yes	Yes	Yes

Annie tried to scratch each piece of rock with her fingernail, a coin and a nail. This kind of test is called **a scratch test**.

Write the name of each type of rock in the correct box on this hardness line.

One has been done for you.

Sandstone

Soft

Hard

Water and rock

Hannah tested five pieces of rock to see if they soaked up water. She poured a little water on to each piece of rock. Then she made a table of her results.

Type of rock	Soaked up water?
Chalk	Yes
Granite	No
Marble	No
Limestone	Yes
Sandstone	Yes

1 The rocks which soaked up water were

_____

_____

2 The rocks which did not soak up water were

_____

_____

3 Do you think it would be a good idea to build a house of chalk? What is your reason?

_____

_____

Rocks that soak up water are called **permeable** rocks.

Rocks that do not soak up water are called **impermeable** rocks.

Rock properties

Different rocks have different **properties**. For instance, some are hard, some soak up water and some split into layers easily.

1 Annie has found five pieces of rock. Draw a line to link each piece of rock to its properties.

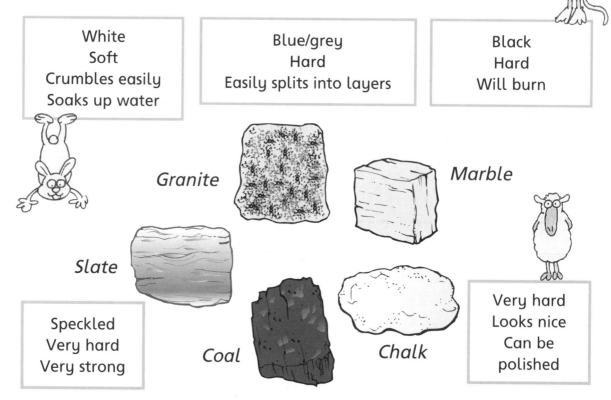

White
Soft
Crumbles easily
Soaks up water

Blue/grey
Hard
Easily splits into layers

Black
Hard
Will burn

Granite

Marble

Slate

Speckled
Very hard
Very strong

Coal

Chalk

Very hard
Looks nice
Can be polished

2 Can you think of something each of these rocks could be used for? Here are some words to help you.

Drawing   Fires   Walls   Roofs   Statues

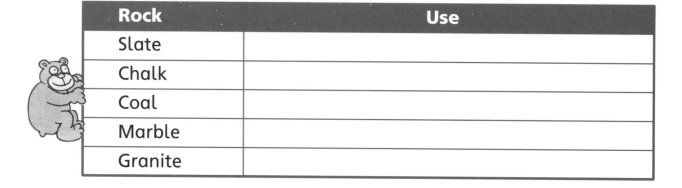

Rock	Use
Slate	
Chalk	
Coal	
Marble	
Granite	

Feel the soil

Did you know that there are many different **kinds of soil**?
This sorting tree contains information about four kinds.
Have a look at the sorting tree, then answer the questions.

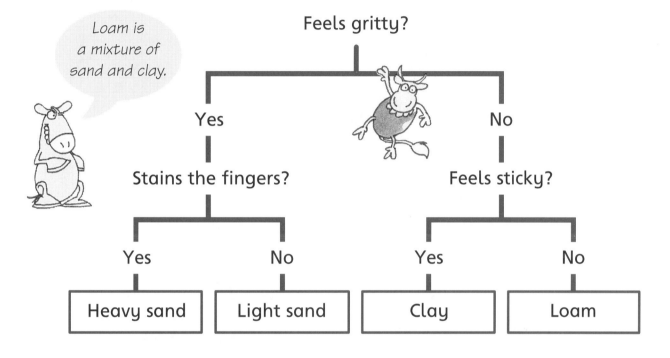

Loam is a mixture of sand and clay.

Feels gritty?

Yes — Stains the fingers?
Yes → Heavy sand
No → Light sand

No — Feels sticky?
Yes → Clay
No → Loam

1 Does heavy sand stain the fingers? _____

2 Does clay feel sticky? _____

3 Does light sand feel gritty? _____

4 Does loam feel sticky? _____

5 Use the sorting tree to find two properties for each type of soil.

Type of soil	Property I	Property 2
Heavy sand	Feels gritty	
Light sand		
Clay		
Loam		Does not feel sticky

Sieving soil

Soil is made up of **particles** of different sizes.

The largest particles are stones.

The smallest are as fine as dust.

Hannah has been using sieves to separate some soil.

She started with a wide-meshed sieve. This caught the large stones.

Hannah put the large stones in a separate pile, then sieved the soil again.

This time, she used a sieve with a medium mesh.

1 Where did the medium-sized particles end up?

_____

2 Where did the smallest particles end up?

_____

3 How many samples did Hannah end up with altogether?

_____

4 Hannah weighed the samples. She made a table to show her results.

Large	Medium	Small
450 grams	350 grams	200 grams

This row shows the weight of each sample.

Draw these results on the graph below.

One column has been drawn for you.

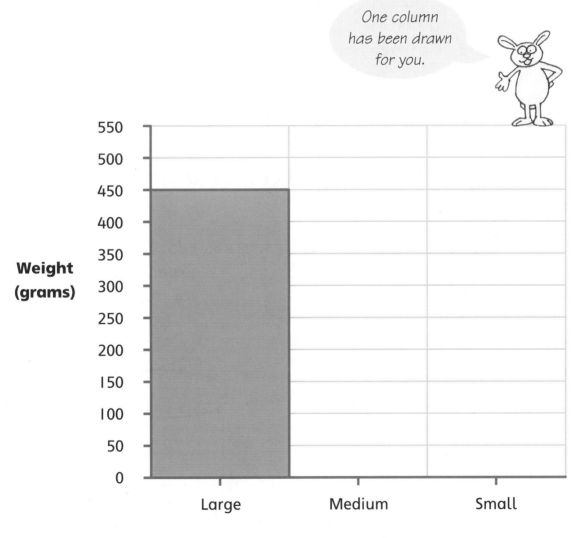

Weight (grams)

Particle size

Soil separation

Ask a grown-up to help with this activity.

Using a sieve is just one way of **separating soil**.
Here's another method that you can try for yourself.

What you need

- A spade or trowel
- A clear plastic container with a lid
- Some soil
- Some water

What to do

1. Collect some soil using the spade or trowel.

Don't dig up the flowers!

2. Put it into the clear plastic container.

3. Add some water to make the container about half full.

4. Screw on the lid.

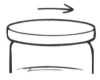

5. Shake the container until the soil and water are mixed together.

6. Leave the experiment for about an hour.

---

1 The soil should settle in layers. Draw a picture of the soil in your container, showing the different layers.

2 Where are the largest particles? _____

3 Where are the smallest particles? _____

Magnetic attraction

1 Do you think these things would be attracted by a **magnet**?
Put a tick or a cross in each box.

Object	Attracted?
Paper clip	
Saucepan	
Book	
Metal spoon	
Pencil	

2 Think of three more things that will be picked up by a magnet.

_____

_____

3 Think of three more things that will not be picked up.

_____

_____

_____

_____

If you have a magnet yourself, you can test your answers, then try question 4.

4 Hold a selection of coins close to a magnet. Were they attracted to it?

_____

Now try picking up an empty drinks can with a magnet.
What does this experiment tell you?

_____

Do you think all metal things are magnetic?

_____

Weak or strong?

Some magnets are stronger than others.

Hannah has been testing the **strength** of four magnets.

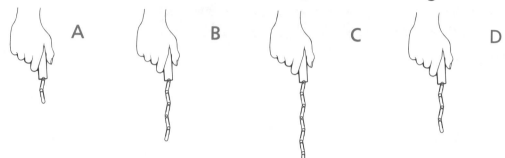

A   B   C   D

1 Complete this graph to show the results of the experiment.

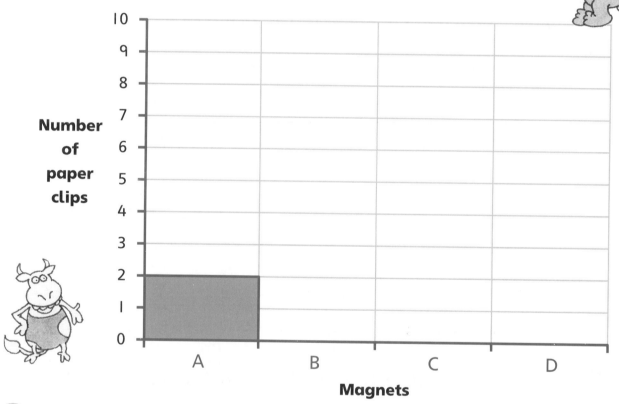

2 Zak is going to try the same experiment. Here are the paper clips he has collected. What should he do to make sure the experiment is fair?

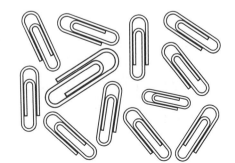

_____

_____

Magnet sort

Hannah wants to find out what happens when you put two magnets next to each other.

*If two magnets try to stick together, we say they **attract** each other.*

*If two magnets push away from each other, we say they **repel** each other.*

1 Look at each pair of magnets. Do the magnets repel or attract each other?

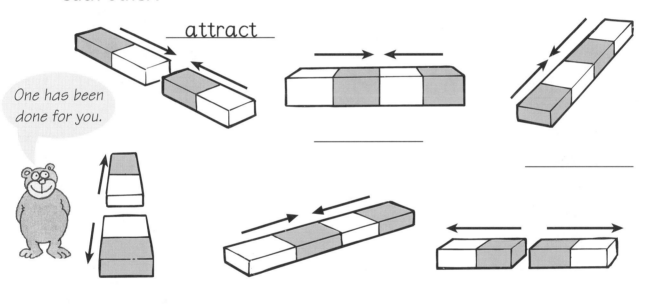

attract

One has been done for you.

_____

_____

_____   _____   _____

Look at the ends of the magnets.

Each magnet has a North end and a South end.

In the picture on this page, the North ends are all coloured in.

2 What do you notice about the magnets that attract each other?

_____

3 What do you notice about the magnets that repel each other?

_____

Uses of magnets

Magnets are useful in our homes and classrooms because magnets are able to push and pull other metals.

Here are some pictures of some of the uses of magnets.

In the box below each picture explain how the magnet is useful.

Think of another.

Magic magnets

Do **magnets** still attract through other materials?

Let's do two tests to find out.

You will need

- a magnet
- a paper clip
- a plastic beaker
- paper
- water
- a large piece of card

magnet | paper clip

What to do

1. Fill the plastic beaker almost full of water.
2. Drop a paper clip into the beaker so it sinks to the bottom of the beaker.
3. Use the magnet to get the paper clip up from the bottom of the beaker.

1 Can you get the paper clip out of the water without getting your fingers wet? _____

2 What does this tell you about the magnet?

_____

_____

What to do

1. Put the paper clip on the card.
2. Hold the magnet underneath the card.
3. Try to move the paper clip without touching it.

3 What does this tell you about the magnet?

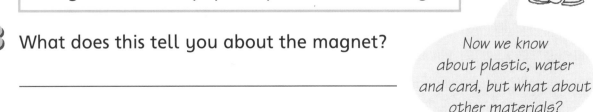

Now we know about plastic, water and card, but what about other materials?

_____

_____

35

Springs

Springs are very common although they are sometimes quite difficult to see.

Look at the pictures below. Some of the objects have springs inside and some of them don't.

1 Put a ✓ beside the items which you think contain a spring.

2 Choose three of the items above that do have springs in them. Explain what the spring does.

_____

_____

_____

_____

_____

_____

Simply stretching

An elastic band is able to go back to the same shape after it has been **squashed** or **stretched**. The stretched elastic pushes back on the object stretching it. We say the elastic band **exerts a force**. This force can be used to make things move. This is how a catapult works.

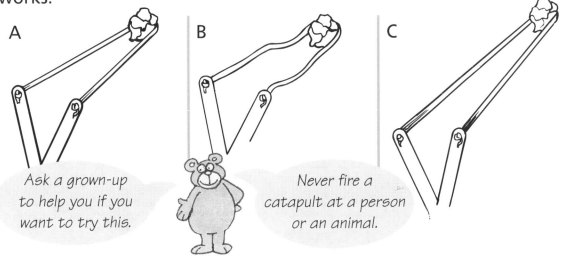

A   B   C

Ask a grown-up to help you if you want to try this.

Never fire a catapult at a person or an animal.

1. Look at the pictures above. Which catapult would make the paper go furthest? Put them in order starting with the best one.

_____   _____   _____

Springs are like elastic bands because they also go back to the same shape and push back on the object pushing them.

2. Write push or pull under each of the pictures below.

3. Draw arrows on each picture to show the direction of the force.

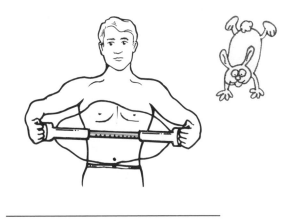

_____   _____

Jack-in-the-box

1 What happens to Jack when you open the lid of his box?

_____

_____

_____

2 Why does this happen?

_____

_____

_____

3 What happens to the spring?

_____

_____

_____

4 What do you have to do to get Jack back in his box?

_____

_____

5 What happens to the spring?

_____

_____

6 Is it easy or hard to shut the lid? Why?

_____

_____

Plants for food

Many **plant**s give food to humans and animals. Some plants are grown especially for this.

1 Tick the boxes to show which plants give food to humans.

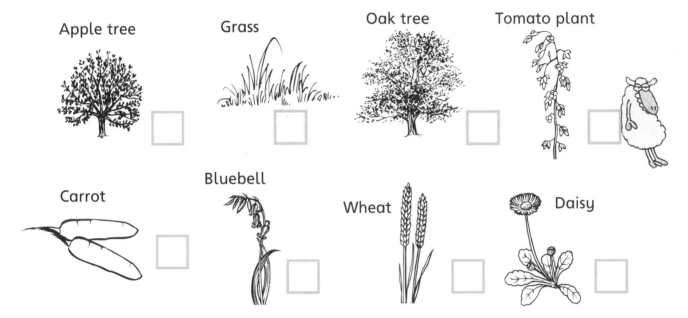

Apple tree Grass Oak tree Tomato plant

Carrot Bluebell Wheat Daisy

2 Make a list of plants that give us food and a separate list of plants that don't.

Plants that give us food	Plants that don't give us food
Peas	Daffodils
Onions	

Some have been done to get you started.

Have a look in the kitchen cupboards at home to help you.

Plant parts

1 These labels show the names of **parts of plants**. The writing on the labels has been jumbled up. Sort out the writing, then join each label to the correct **part** of the plant.

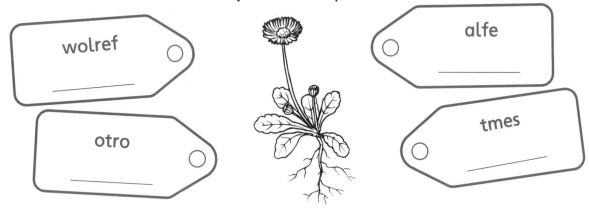

wolref

_____

otro

_____

alfe

_____

tmes

_____

2 Not all plants look the same. Write the same names on these new labels. Join each one to the correct part of the plant.

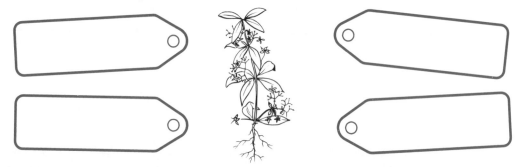

3 If you have a pot-plant at home, try drawing a picture of it here. Don't forget to add some labels.

Just draw the parts that you can see above the soil.

Growing seeds

Ask a grown-up to help you with this activity.

Try **growing** some **cress seeds** in four different ways.

You will need

- Four plastic pots
- A packet of cress seeds
- Water
- Cotton wool
- Compost
- Sand
- Tissues

If you don't have any compost or sand, just use tissues and cotton wool.

What to do

1. Fill the pots, one with wet cotton wool, one with compost, one with sand and one with wet tissues.
2. Sprinkle some seeds into each pot.
3. Put the pots on a warm, sunny window sill.
4. Give each pot a little water every day.

1 Guess which seeds will grow first. Write your predictions in the table below (1 = first; 4 = last).

2 Now watch what happens over the next few days. Write your results in the table.

Ask a grown-up to tell you when the cress is ready to eat.

3 Write in the table how long it takes for the cress to be ready to eat.

Wash the cress before you eat it.

	Which will grow first? My predictions	Which grew first? My results	How many days until it's ready to eat?
Cotton wool			
Compost			
Sand			
Wet tissues			

Fair test?

Class 5 have been growing some beans in the classroom. They wanted to find out the best conditions for growing.

> Table 1 put their beans in the fridge and watered them.
> Table 2 put their beans on the windowsill in the sun and watered them.
> Table 3 didn't water their beans and put them on the windowsill.
> Table 4 put their beans in a cupboard and watered them.

Class 5 wanted to make sure that the tests were **fair**.

1 What were the conditions where each plant was growing? Fill in the chart.

Plants need light, warmth and water to help them grow well.

Put a tick for the conditions that the places had.

Put a cross for the conditions that the places didn't have.

Table	Light	Warmth	Water
Table 1	✗	✗	✓
Table 2			
Table 3			
Table 4			

2 Make a list of the things that Class 5 would have to do to make it a fair test.

Use the chart to help you.

(a) _____

(b) _____

(c) _____

After 10 days Class 5 measured their beans.
Here are the results.

Table	Height of beans
Table 1	2 cm
Table 2	20 cm
Table 3	4 cm
Table 4	8 cm

3 Draw a graph of their results.

What will you write here?

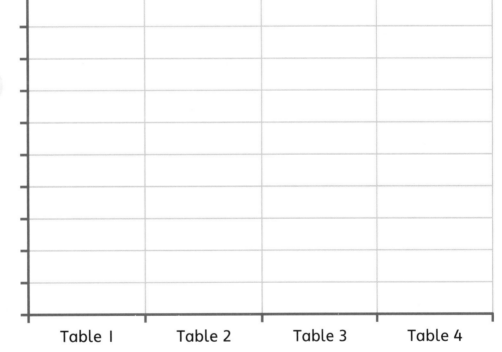

Table 1   Table 2   Table 3   Table 4

4 Which Table's beans grew the most? _____

Why? _____

_____

5 Which Table's beans grew the least? _____

Why? _____

_____

Thirsty plants

1 Use these words to fill in the spaces.

parts

flowers

droopy

firm

water

The stem supports the _____ and leaves. It carries

_____ up a plant to its different _____ . When a plant

has enough water, the stem feels _____ . When a plant does

not have enough water, the stem feels soft and _____ .

2 This plant has plenty of _____ .

3 Draw a plant that does not have enough water.

Going up!

Ask a grown-up to help you.

You will need

- a beaker of water
- some food colouring
- a white carnation or a stick of celery

What to do

1. Put the stick of celery (or the stem of the carnation) in the beaker of water.
2. Add a few drops of food colouring to the water, then leave the experiment for a little while.

1 Colour one of the pictures here to show what happens.

2 What do you think is happening? Explain it in your own words.

_____

_____

_____

45

Leaf hunt

Ask a grown-up to help you find the leaves.

Leaves come in many different shapes and sizes. How many different kinds can you find?

1 Collect as many differently shaped leaves as possible.

2 Draw a picture of each one at the bottom of these pages.

3 Look carefully at each leaf and describe it. Here are some words to help you.

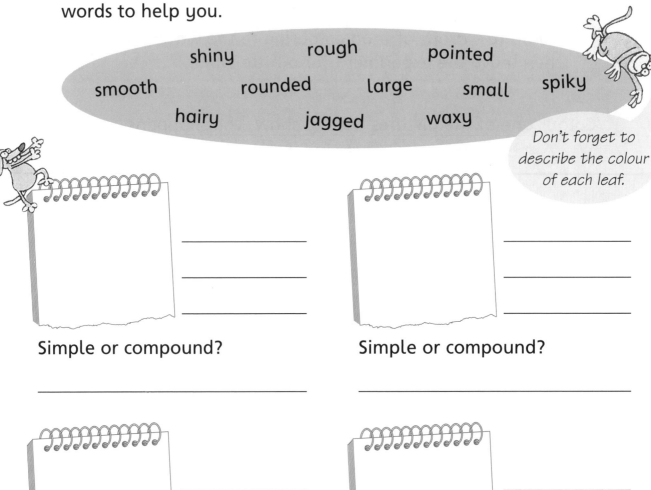

shiny   rough   pointed

smooth   rounded   large   small   spiky

hairy   jagged   waxy

Don't forget to describe the colour of each leaf.

Simple or compound?

_____

Simple or compound?

_____

Simple or compound?

Simple or compound?

4 There are two main types of leaf: **simple** and **compound**. For each leaf you have drawn, say whether it is simple or compound.

Simple or compound?

_____

Simple or compound?

_____

Simple or compound?

_____

Simple or compound?

_____

Leaves and light

Leaves are very important to plants. They provide the plant with the food it needs to survive. This is because they are able to turn sunlight energy into food energy. What happens if a plant doesn't get enough **light**?

You will need

- a collection of green leaves
- coloured tape or masking tape

What to do

1. Stick some coloured tape in the shape of a cross on each leaf.
2. Put the leaves in a sunny position.
3. After a few days, carefully peel off the sticky tape.

1 Describe what happened.

_____

_____

_____

Draw a picture of your leaves.

Jessica planted some seeds. She wanted to see what would happen if she gave them different amounts of light.

2 Join up the pictures of the plants to where you think they were grown.

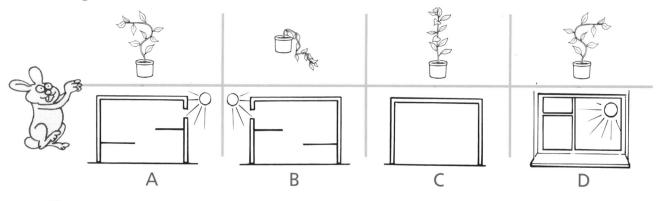

A   B   C   D

3 Where did Jessica's seeds grow best? _____

Bits and pieces

1   This plant has lost all its leaves. Find the right place for each leaf.

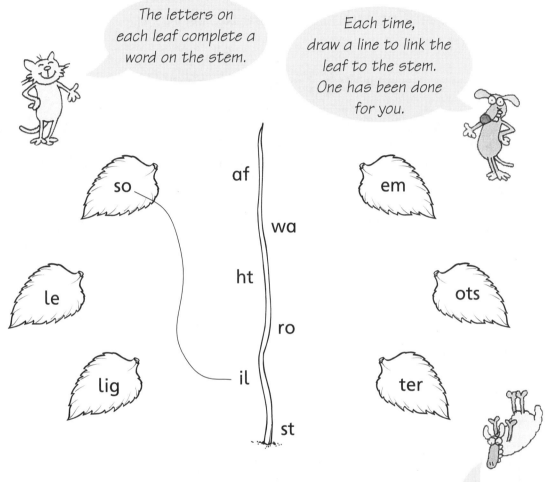

The letters on each leaf complete a word on the stem.

Each time, draw a line to link the leaf to the stem. One has been done for you.

2   Write a sentence for each word you have found.
For each thing, say how it helps a plant grow.

One has been done for you.

Stem	The stem supports the flowers and leaves.

Materials hunt

1 In this word search, you should be able to find the names of eight **materials**. Ring or colour them as you find them. Here are the words to look out for.

A material is something you use to make things.

metal   wood

rock   rubber   paper

plastic   glass

fabric

The words read downwards or across from left to right.

d	z	m	f	j	f	x	c	v	m
n	g	f	u	a	a	l	h	r	e
t	l	x	l	d	b	j	l	u	t
t	a	q	c	t	r	u	p	b	a
o	s	g	g	z	i	e	a	b	l
i	s	v	m	p	c	n	p	e	o
o	q	t	a	e	j	j	e	r	w
n	w	o	o	d	r	t	r	w	e
r	o	c	k	s	b	u	k	o	o
s	l	p	p	l	a	s	t	i	c

2 Think of four other materials and write their names.

_____ _____ _____ _____

3 Now go on a materials hunt in your home. Try to find objects made from each of the materials in this chart. How many can you find for each material?

An example has been filled in to help you.

wood	metal
_____	____ spoon ____
_____	_____
_____	_____
_____	_____

plastic	paper
_____	_____
_____	_____
_____	_____
_____	_____

fabric	rock
_____	_____
_____	_____
_____	_____
_____	_____

rubber	glass
_____	_____
_____	_____
_____	_____
_____	_____

Finding properties

When you're choosing the best material for something, you have to think about its **properties**. For instance, is it strong, shiny, transparent, bouncy or rigid?

1 Draw a line to link each property in this chart with its meaning.

One has been done for you.

transparent	soaks up water
strong	see-through
rigid	doesn't let water pass through
flexible	can't change its shape
absorbent	attracted to a magnet
waterproof	has bumps on its surface
shiny	bendy
magnetic	reflects the light
smooth	hard to break
rough	has no bumps on its surface

2 Sort these properties into pairs with opposite meanings.

flexible   rigid   strong   breakable

waterproof   hard   absorbent   soft

For example, rough is the opposite of smooth.

3 Complete this table by ticking the most important properties of each material.

An example for wood has been done to help you.

	Transparent	Strong	Hard	Soft	Flexible	Breakable	Rigid	Absorbent	Waterproof	Shiny
Wood		✓	✓				✓			
Metal										
Plastic										
Paper										
Fabric										
Rock										
Rubber										
Glass										

4 Which material is hard and shiny?

_____

5 Which material is absorbent and flexible?

_____

6 Which material is rigid, waterproof and transparent?

_____

Bouncing up

Zak has been doing an experiment to find out if some surfaces are more bouncy than others.

If a surface is bouncy, this is one of its **properties**.

He dropped a ball from a height of 1 metre onto different surfaces. Each time, he measured how far it bounced up.

He made a table to show his results.

Surface	Height of bounce
carpet	18 cm
stone floor	32 cm
vinyl floor	22 cm
tarmac	28 cm

1 Draw columns on this graph to show the height of each bounce.

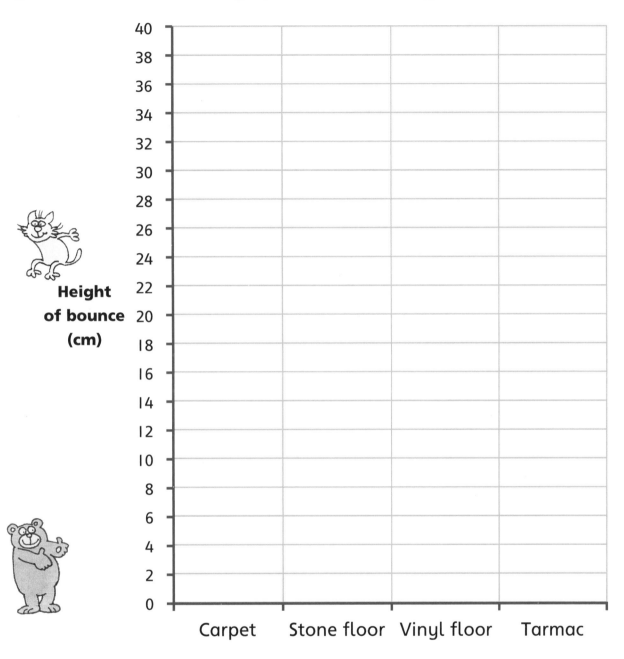

2 Which surface gave the highest bounce? Why?

_____

_____

3 Which surface gave the lowest bounce? Why?

_____

_____

Sorting properties

Write the names of these materials in the correct places in the charts.

metal   plastic   paper
wood   glass
        rubber   Plasticine
cardboard   rock
        leather   fabric   concrete

Some materials fit into both charts.

	hard	soft
rigid		
flexible		

	rough	smooth
absorbent		
waterproof		

Best material?

1   Each of these things is made from a different material. Think of two **properties** that make each material right for the job.

Here are some words to help you:

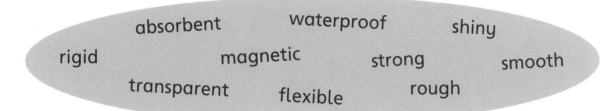

absorbent   waterproof   shiny

rigid   magnetic   strong   smooth

transparent   flexible   rough

concrete post

_____

_____

glass measuring jug

_____

_____

leather belt

_____

_____

plastic raincoat

_____

_____

2   The objects below need materials with special properties. Draw lines to match each object to the correct property.

A thermal insulator does not let heat pass through.

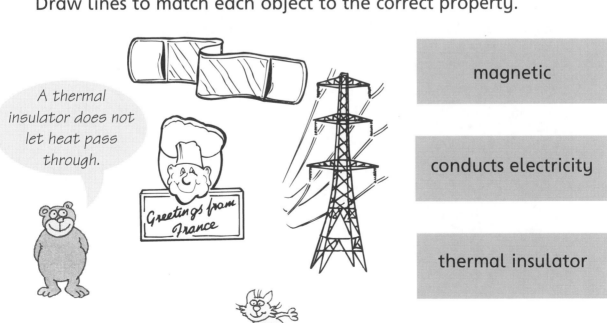

magnetic

conducts electricity

thermal insulator

57

Mix-up!

Look at these objects. There has been a mix-up at the factory, so they are not made of the correct material.

For each material, say why the material is not suitable, and suggest a better one.

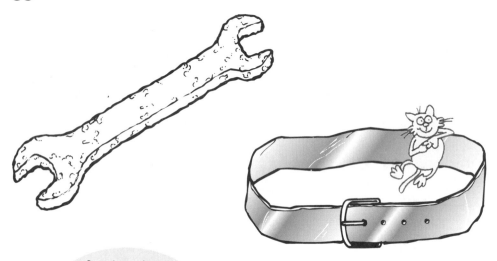

One has been done for you to show you what to do.

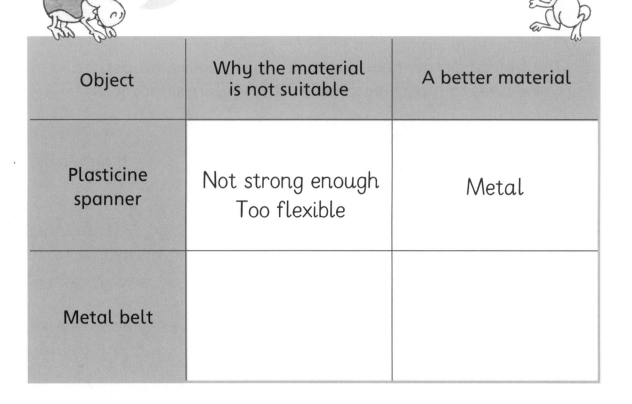

Object	Why the material is not suitable	A better material
Plasticine spanner	Not strong enough Too flexible	Metal
Metal belt		

Object	Why the material is not suitable	A better material
Rubber towel		
Metal lifebelt		
Plastic saucepan		
Wooden mirror		

59

The bicycle

A **bicycle** has many working parts.

So that each part can work properly, they are made of different materials. The materials have **properties** that make them right for the job.

1 Name each part of the bicycle. Use these words to help you.

pedals   saddle   wheels
brakes   handlebars   tyres
                                          bell
    chain   frame   brake cables

2 Each part has a special job to do. Explain what jobs these parts do.

saddle _____

brakes _____

pedals _____

tyres _____

frame _____

3 Which parts of the bicycle have these properties?

Property	Parts of the bicycle
hard	
smooth	
flexible	
thin	
soft	
strong	
reflects the light	
changes shape	
reduces friction	
increases friction	

4 Choose three of the parts of the bicycle. What are they made from? Why has that material been used?

Part of the bicycle	Material it is made from	Why that material has been used

Vocabulary

These are all words that you need to know to be a good scientist. See if you can fit them into the word maze.

Start with the longest words!

---

4 letter words

clay   diet   hard
iron   sand
stem

5 letter words

molar   plant
repel   roots
steel

6 letter words

canine   growth
leaves   opaque
shadow   strong

7 letter words

attract   incisor
texture

8 letter words

flexible   magnetic

9 letter words

absorbent   direction

11 letter words

transparent

Answers and Hints

In some instances there may be more than one possible answer so you may need to check that the answer your child has given is reasonable. As long as your child's answer makes sense and has shown they understand the question, you should mark it right. Sometimes the question will ask them to express an opinion, to make a prediction or to create their own piece of work. When marking your child's efforts please remember that encouragement is always more helpful than criticism.

PAGE 5
1 (ticked things) Sun, Torch, Ceiling light fixture, Bedside lamp, Study lamp   2 Stained glass window, Window, Fish bowl

PAGES 6 & 7
1 The shape your child draws will depend on in what direction they shone the torch on the object.   2 Play with your child to see what shadows you can make with your hands.   3 The shadow is drawn in the wrong direction (the Sun is on the right-hand side).   4 Check that your child has drawn the Sun in a sensible position above each object.

PAGES 8 & 9
1 the size of the shadow changes   2 Your child should understand that moving the puppet nearer to and further away from the torch will change the size of the shadow.   3 the shadow gets bigger   4 the shadow gets smaller   5 Your child should understand that the shadow is formed because the puppet stops the light from the torch reaching the wall.   6 (top to bottom) false, true, false, true   7 The last drawing is the correct one (with the light bulb over the boy's head).

PAGE 10
1 (ticked photos) first (Big Ben) and last (Tower Bridge)   2 (a) true, (b) false, (c) false, (d) true, (e) true

PAGE 11
Check that your child has completed the bar chart correctly (at heights corresponding to (left to right) 50 cm, 30 cm, 10 cm, 30 cm, 50 cm, 70 cm and 90 cm). Ask your child to say what the bar chart means (that shadows start long, become short and then become long again during each day).

PAGE 12
1 (missing word, in order) spins, Sun, East, West   2 day   3 night   4 Check your child understands that day and night is caused because the Earth turns round, and that those places facing the Sun are in day time, and those facing away from the Sun are in night time.

PAGE 13
1 (connected animals and foods) Sheep–Grass, Bluetit–Seeds, Tiger–Meat, Panda–Leaves   2 (ringed foods, top to bottom) meat, grass, leaves, leaves, insects, insects, fish, leaves, grass, fish   3 they would die (Check that your child understands that all animals need food to survive.)

PAGES 14 & 15
1 (fruit) Apples, Oranges, Grapes, Banana   2 (vegetables) Potatoes, Broccoli, Carrots, Peas, Onions   3 (breakfast cereals) Cornflakes, Muesli   4 (dairy) Milk, Cheese, Butter, Yoghurt   5 (meat or fish) Sausages, Fish, Chicken, Fish Fingers   6 Sugar, Honey (Check that your child understands that these are both sugars.)

PAGE 16
1 Check what your child has written – can you think of anything that they've forgotten?   2 Your child should understand that a human's diet is much more varied than an animal's and includes many foods not found naturally (like burgers and ice cream!).

PAGE 17

z	a	y	t	h	g	r	e	n	e	r	g	y	d
m	o	v	i	n	g	b	c	s	e	v	a	m	c
a	w	m	l	f	a	g	m	g	k	u	d	a	l
t	g	r	o	w	t	d	o	r	u	j	r	a	i
u	e	b	t	y	u	a	f	o	n	i	t	e	m
r	g	e	w	m	d	n	y	w	o	u	d	s	b
n	x	n	e	o	g	c	x	t	i	r	u	n	o
s	c	d	r	v	i	e	p	h	n	r	i	f	
h	e	c	d	e	f	t	h	k	i	m	b	d	l
o	g	l	s	m	t	f	j	s	a	o	p	n	u
h	o	p	l	e	s	a	u	j	w	a	l	k	b
d	f	c	i	n	k	n	m	c	h	u	n	s	h
s	u	s	d	t	i	r	p	c	p	u	l	l	d
p	h	e	e	i	p	f	l	l	b	t	r	a	s

PAGE 18
(animals with pointed teeth, like a lion) fox, shark, dog, crocodile; (animals with flat teeth, like a horse) cow, rabbit, giraffe, sheep
Your child should understand that animals that eat other animals have sharp teeth, and that animals that eat grass and vegetables have flat teeth.

PAGE 19
The skulls with sharp teeth should be coloured red (they are the meat-eaters), the skulls with flat teeth should be coloured green (they are the plant-eaters). Your child's answers should show that they understand what animals with sharp and flat teeth eat.

PAGE 20
1 (connected sentences) New-born babies–have no teeth, Young children–have small milk teeth, The milk teeth–are pushed out as we grow up, Adult teeth–replace the milk teeth   2 (incisors) 8   3 (canines) 4   4 (molars) 8–12 (adults have up to 20 molars (when you count the wisdom teeth) but at this age your child will probably have 2 or 3 molars on each side of each jaw)   5 20–24 at this age (but up to 32 in adults)

PAGE 21

c	r	s	h	f	a	b	i	t	e	e	r	c
d	z	g	n	a	w	t	e	n	t	w	i	h
a	n	t	i	n	r	i	n	o	g	f	r	e
c	r	u	n	c	h	e	i	l	o	v	e	w
s	c	a	b	r	w	y	b	g	b	c	t	r
a	u	t	m	y	d	h	b	j	b	s	e	m
m	t	e	u	g	e	j	l	n	l	w	a	u
u	t	o	n	e	v	v	e	i	e	o	r	t
m	o	m	c	t	o	q	a	f	a	b	h	i
i	w	d	h	w	u	f	c	r	u	s	h	x
a	b	a	r	y	r	e	e	f	c	k	b	r
g	r	i	n	d	e	a	z	q	y	h	e	y
s	a	i	d	e	s	l	i	c	e	t	i	n

PAGE 22
1 (circled foods) cake, biscuit, sugar, cola, sweets, chocolate   2 (circled foods) carrot, apple, pear, tomato, orange   3 Your child should say that they should eat less bad foods, eat more good foods and brush their teeth twice a day.

PAGE 23
1 (coloured objects) statue, gravel path, bridge, slate roof, rocks by pond   2 Check that your child has written sensible answers (possible answers: earth, sea, rivers, plants, roads).

PAGE 24
(hardness line, left to right) Chalk, Limestone, (Sandstone), Granite

PAGE 25
1 Chalk, Limestone, Sandstone   2 Granite, Marble   3 Your child should understand that building a house of chalk is not a good idea – think what would happen if it rained!

PAGE 26
1 (connect rocks and properties (only the first property of each rock is given in the answer)) White–Chalk, Blue/grey–Slate, Black–Coal, Speckled–Granite, Very hard–Marble   2 (uses, top to bottom) Roofs, Drawing, Fire, Statues, Walls (your child may have thought of some other uses as well)

PAGE 27
1 Yes   2 Yes   3 Yes   4 No   5 (property 1, top to bottom) Feels gritty, Feels gritty, Does not feel gritty, Does not feel gritty; (property 2, top to bottom) Stains the fingers, Does not stain the fingers, Feels sticky, Does not feel sticky

PAGES 28 & 29
1 caught in the second sieve (with the medium mesh)   2 in the pan   3 3   4 Check that your child has completed the bar chart correctly (at heights corresponding to 350 grams (Medium) and 200 grams (Small)) and that they understand how the different sizes of particles would be separated by using two sieves.

PAGE 30
1 Check that your child has drawn the layers accurately.   2 at the bottom (the largest particles are heavier and will sink)   3 at the top

PAGE 31
1 (top to bottom) tick, tick, cross, tick, cross (most saucepans would be attracted by a magnet, although ones made of aluminium would not)   2 Check that your child has thought of three things that would be attracted by a magnet (possible answers: nail, pin, fork, knife, needle)   3 There are lots of non-magnetic things (such as paper, plants and teddy bears!).   4 Some coins are magnetic, some are not (newer 'copper' coins are actually made with steel (which is magnetic) in the middle). Some drinks cans are made out of steel, which is magnetic, but most are made out of aluminium, which is not. Your child should understand that not all metals are magnetic (and it's not always obvious just by looking!).

PAGE 32
1 Check that your child has completed the bar chart correctly (at heights corresponding to (left to right) 5, 7 and 4 paper clips).
2 Zak should only use paper clips that are the same size

PAGE 33
1 (top row, left to right) attract, attract; (bottom row) repel, attract, repel   2 magnets attract when a North end and a South end (different ends) are put together   3 magnets repel when two North ends or two South ends (similar ends) are put together

PAGE 34
Check your child's answers – have they understood in each case where the magnet is, what it is attracting, and why this is a good use of a magnet?   Check that your child has thought of sensible use of a magnet (such as a fridge magnet) and has explained how the magnet is being used.

PAGE 35
1 yes (your child should be able to get the paper clip out using the magnet)   2 the magnet still attracts metal through plastic and water   3 the magnet still attracts metal through card

PAGE 36
1 (ticked things) toaster, retractable ball-point pen, mattress, trampoline, bicycle seat, armchair, hole punch   2 Check that your child understands what the spring in the three objects they chose does: (toaster) lifts up the bread; (pen) pushes out the point; (mattress) adjusts to whoever lies on the mattress, making it more comfortable; (trampoline) springs the trampolinist back up into the air; (bicycle seat) cushions the cyclist (like the mattress); (arm chair) adjusts to whoever sits in the chair, making it more comfortable; (hole punch) springs the lever back up after holes are punched

PAGE 37
1 (best to worst) C, A, B   2 both pictures show a 'pushing' force   3 the finger pushes down; the man pushes on both ends

PAGE 38
1 the puppet springs up   2 opening the lid lets the spring push the puppet up   3 the spring gets longer   4 push down on the puppet and the lid   5 the spring gets shorter   6 it is hard to shut the lid because you have to push to shorten the spring (you have to apply force to shorten the spring)

PAGE 39
1 (ticked plants) Apple tree, Tomato plant, Carrot, Wheat
2 Check that your child has written sensible lists of plants.

PAGE 40
1 (correct labels) flower, root, leaf, stem (Check that your child has connected the labels correctly.)   2 Check that your child has connected the labels correctly.   3 Check your child's drawing – have they labelled their plant correctly?

PAGE 41
After your child has done the experiment, ask them about how their predictions were different from their results – if there were any differences, why do they think this was?

PAGES 42 & 43
1 (Light column, missing ticks/crosses, top to bottom) tick, tick, cross; (Warmth column) tick, tick, tick; (Water column) tick, cross, tick
2 To make the test fair the children would need to make sure the beans were all the same (type and size), use the same amount of water when watering them, and check that the windowsill and cupboard were the same temperature.   3 Check that your child has completed the bar chart correctly (at heights corresponding to 2 cm, 20 cm, 4 cm and 8 cm; the best way for your child to label the left-hand axis is to make each division equal to 2 cm).   4 Table 2; the beans were given light, warmth and water   5 Table 1; the beans were given no light and no warmth (they had water, but without light and warmth they couldn't grow much)

PAGE 44
1 (missing words, in order) flowers, water, parts, firm, droopy   2 water   3 Check that your child has drawn a very droopy plant!

PAGE 45
Your child should have found that the colour moves up the plant (and into the petals, in the case of the carnation) – your child's drawing should match what actually happened when they did the experiment. Check that your child has understood that water moves up inside plants so that water reaches all the different parts.

PAGES 46 & 47
Check your child's drawing and answers – check that they understand the difference between simple and compound leaves.

PAGE 48
1 the part of the leaf covered by the tape went pale (Your child's drawing should show that the leaf's colour went pale underneath the tape.)   2 pictures (left to right) connected to these drawings in this order) B, C, D, A   3 in the window

PAGE 49
1 (connected words) le–af, lig–ht, st–em, ro–ots, wa–ter   2 (possible answers) Soil – provides water and minerals; Leaf – collects light and warmth, and makes food; Light – helps the plant make food; Roots – collect water from the ground; Water – keeps plant healthy and stops it wilting

PAGES 50 & 51

d	z	m	f	j	f	x	c	v	m
n	g	f	u	a	a	l	h	r	e
t	l	x	l	d	b	j	l	u	t
t	a	q	c	t	r	u	p	b	a
o	s	g	g	z	i	e	a	b	l
i	s	v	m	p	c	n	p	e	o
o	q	t	a	e	j	j	e	r	w
n	w	o	o	d	r	t	r	w	e
r	o	c	k	s	b	u	k	o	o
s	l	p	p	l	a	s	t	i	c

2 Check that your child has thought of four other materials (possible answers: leather, cardboard, concrete, Plasticine)   3 How many did your child find? (Check that they have identified the materials of the household items correctly.)

PAGES 52 & 53
1 (connect sentences) strong–hard to break, rigid–can't change its shape, flexible–bendy, absorbent–soaks up water, waterproof–doesn't let water pass through, shiny–reflects the light, magnetic–attracted to a magnet, smooth–has no bumps on its surface, rough–has bumps on its surface   2 (sorted pairs, any order) flexible–rigid, waterproof–absorbent, hard–soft, strong–breakable   3 (ticked properties for each material) Metal – strong, hard, rigid, waterproof, shiny; Plastic – soft, flexible, waterproof (but some plastics are also strong, hard, rigid, transparent, shiny (or a mixture of these properties)); Paper – soft, flexible, breakable, absorbent (can be shiny); Fabric – soft, flexible, absorbent (can be shiny); Rock – strong, hard, rigid (some are also absorbent, some are waterproof); Rubber – strong, soft, flexible, waterproof; Glass – transparent, hard, breakable, rigid, waterproof, shiny   4 metal or glass   5 paper or fabric   6 glass (some plastics can also have these properties)

PAGES 54 & 55
1 Check that your child has completed the bar chart correctly (at heights corresponding to (left to right) 18 cm, 32 cm, 22 cm and 28 cm).   2 stone floor; it is a hard surface   3 carpet; it is a soft surface

PAGE 56
top chart: (top left) concrete, metal, rock, glass, wood; (bottom right) Plasticine, cardboard, rubber, fabric, leather, paper (plastic can have all four properties, so should be written in each box)
bottom chart: (top left) wood, fabric, concrete; (top right) cardboard, paper; (bottom left) leather; (bottom right) Plasticine, metal, rubber, glass, plastic (rock can have all four properties, so should be written in each box)

PAGE 57
1 (properties) concrete post – strong, rigid; glass measuring jug – waterproof, transparent; leather belt – strong, flexible; plastic raincoat – waterproof, flexible (Your child may have chosen slightly different answers.)   2 (connected pairs) oven gloves–thermal insulator; fridge magnet–magnetic; electricity cables–conducts electricity

PAGES 58 & 59
There are many possible answers; check your child has given sensible reasons and suggestions; (metal belt – why the material is unsuitable) not flexible enough, (a better material) leather; (rubber towel) waterproof, fabric; (metal lifebelt) too heavy, rubber; (plastic saucepan) will melt when it gets hot, metal; (wooden mirror) not reflective, glass

PAGES 60 & 61
1 Check that your child has identified the parts of the bicycle correctly.   2 (possible answers, top to bottom): (saddle) needs to be comfortable to sit on; (brakes) needs to safely slow down and stop the bicycle; (pedals) need to turn round to work the bicycle chain – this moves the bicycle forward; (tyres) need to grip the road; (frame) need to support the cyclist and the rest of the bicycle.   3 (possible answers, top to bottom): (hard) frame, bell; (smooth) saddle; (flexible) tyres; (thin) brake cables; (soft) saddle, tyres; (strong) frame, brake cables; (reflects the light) safety reflector (and shiny metal parts); (changes shape) tyres, saddle; (reduces friction) oil; (increases friction) tyres   4 Check your child has made sensible suggestions for the parts of the bicycle they chose.

PAGE 62
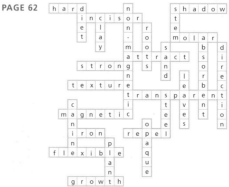